RICHARD STRAUSS

DON JUAN

Symphonic Poem
Sinfonische Dichtung
Op. 20

Ernst Eulenburg Ltd
London · Mainz · New York · Paris · Tokyo · Zürich

RICHARD STRAUSS
Don Juan

There is some confusion as to when Strauss actually began work on *Don Juan*. He himself wrote that on his way to Venice in May 1888 he invented the first themes of *Don Juan* in the courtyard of the San Antonio monastery in Padua. But since the work was certainly completed that summer this allows inconceivably little time for the composition of so elaborate and complex a score, and every biographer has accepted that the first drafts were sketched in the autumn of 1887.

Strauss chose the verse play by Nikolaus Lenau as the basis for his study of that great erotic subject, not so much because of Lenau's dramatic handling of the legend, as because of his psychological approach to the notorious woman-hunter. Lenau's *Don Juan* traces the outlines of Don Juan's career from the scene where his brother Don Diego endeavours to fetch him home from his worthless life of sensuality, to the final duel in which he dies not because he is defeated but because he finds victory 'as boring as the whole of life'. In every exploit it subsequently turns out that some great harm has been done, and Don Juan's attitude in the aftermath of catastrophe is summarized when, after he has desecrated a monastery, the Abbot destroys the entire building in his despair. Don Juan turns to his comrade with the words:

That went too far, that I never meant;
He who does evil ever does more than he intends.

Strauss's treatment is reflected by the quotations with which he heads the score. All are spoken by Don Juan himself, the first two coming close together during the opening scene and forming the kernel of Don Juan's arguments for rejecting his brother's pleas that he return home without delay. The first excerpt proclaims his worship of the Isolated Moment:

Fain would I run the magic circle, immeasurably wide, of beautiful woman's manifold charms, in full tempest of enjoyment, to die of a kiss at the mouth of the last one. O my friend, would that I could fly through every place where beauty blossoms, fall on my knees before each one, and, were it but for a moment, conquer . . .

The central and most extended excerpt represents Juan's answer to Diego's warnings of his inevitable end as a beggar:

I shun satiety and the exhaustion of pleasure; I keep myself fresh in the service of beauty; and in offending the individual I crave for my devotion to her kind. The breath of a woman that is as the odour of spring today, may perhaps tomorrow oppress me like the air of a dungeon. When, in my changes, I travel with my love in the wide circle of beautiful women, my love is a different thing for each one; I build no temple out of ruins. Indeed, passion is always and only the new passion; it cannot be carried from this one to that; it must die here and spring anew there, and when it knows itself, then it knows nothing of repentance. As each beauty stands alone in the world, so stands the love which it prefers. Forth and away then, to triumphs ever new, so long as youth's fiery pulses race! . . .

The last passage comes from the closing Supper Scene when, unlike Da Ponte's Don Giovanni, Juan sits gloomily, enveloped in bitter disillusionment. Yet even now he has no regrets and cannot tolerate the weeping and wailings of remorse:

It was a beautiful storm that urged me on; it has spent its rage, and silence now remains. A trance is upon every wish, every hope. Perhaps a thunderbolt from the heights which I condemned struck fatally at my power of love, and suddenly my world became a desert and darkened. And perhaps not; the fuel is all consumed and the hearth is cold and dark.

The three quotations thus contain none of the action of the play. They are purely psychological and illustrate Strauss's aim of depicting Juan's character through his own words. Yet they are only a partial guide to the music which, on the contrary, indulges to some extent in the direct representation of dramatic episodes. There are two full-blown love scenes, a carnival, and a clearly defined section in which, at the height of the duel, the victorious Don Juan throws away his rapier and receives the death thrust. Nothing of all this is indicated in Strauss's avowed programme; yet the seeming disparity underlines Strauss's whole attitude to his subject. *Don Juan* is on the one hand a symphonic movement, fully worked out according to its thematic requirements, while at the same time portraying the development of a human personality through the impact of events much as Strauss had just done in *Macbeth*, the first version of which was completed in the same year, 1888.

Even the form of the work is fundamentally the same as that of *Macbeth*: i.e. a sonata first movement with two major independent episodes inserted into the development. The principal subject (bars 1–6 and 9–16) is a composite theme, all the major features of which are later isolated and extensively developed. This profusion of ideas together presents the figure of Don Juan himself in all his passionate glory and lust for life.

A further theme, first introduced in the bass instruments in bar 40, carries the music impetuously forward and leads to the hero's first flirtatious exploit. This episode has little substance and might even be thought too transitory to qualify if it did not later take its place with the later love affairs in Juan's disillusionment scene (bars 427 et seq.). The theme of its heroine (bars 48–9) is purely capricious and not even the indication *flebile* (plaintive) can suggest that her heart has been touched.

Yet the chromatically descending figure with which she parts from Juan (bar 53, clarinet) was intended by Strauss to represent 'a feeling of satiety in Juan's heart', indicating that an emotional attachment has existed between them. This is established in bars 46–7 which announce *fortissimo* the melody which will later dominate Juan's first true love scene.

With an impatient flourish he tears himself from this unsatisfactory mistress, turns round, and is immediately spellbound at the appearance of a new beauty. Don Juan is deeply stirred and their love scene follows, a tremendous extended section (bars 90–149) whose passion compares only with such sensual exultation as is to be found in the second act of *Tristan*. Strauss used jocularly to say that it was obvious that the girl had red hair.

If the first flirtation fulfilled the role of transition, this section corresponds with the second subject, even the conventional key of the dominant being used. The music rises to a climax of unbearable intensity, subsiding abruptly as the cellos softly interpose Don Juan's opening motif like a question. He has awakened from the oblivion of love and although his mistress attempts to make his dreams continue, they no longer have the power to hold him. In a moment Don Juan is out of reach and away in search of further adventures.

The passage which follows is pure development, building Don Juan's themes to a pitch of frenzy (bars 169–96); then suddenly there is a halt and a new courtship begins. This time the girl's capitulation is less immediate and Don Juan's wooing takes on a note of yearning intensity (bars 197–202) until gradually he overcomes her pitiable resistance and she finally succumbs altogether.

So complete is her devotion, so touching her love, that the question arises as to who this crucial figure in the story can be; yet it is impossible to establish which of Lenau's heroines Strauss had in mind, as there is no comparable episode in the poem. According to at least one version of the legend, it is Donna Anna who is the only serious passion of Don Juan's life, but in Da Ponte his attempts to seduce her are unsuccessful and in Lenau she is scarcely mentioned. At all events there is not the slightest doubt that Strauss is now concerned with Juan's deepest love experience. The section between bars 232 and 306 is one of the great love songs in all music.

The end of the song marks the half-way point of the tone poem and must have caused Strauss some anxiety as to how he should continue. The way he solved the problem made history. This was through the invention of a new motif for Juan, a call for four horns so striking that it remains to this day the theme with which the whole tone poem is immediately associated (bars 314–26). Don Juan is now not merely dashing and impetuous; he is heroic.

Like the earlier mistress, this poor girl clings to Juan, but she has even less power over him than her predecessors and in any case he is by now in full cry. With a dazzling display of orchestral colour Don Juan is in the thick of some wild festivities.

This second development section (bars 351–423) is generally known as the Carnival Scene although the nearest parallel to be found in Lenau is a Masked Ball. There is a new glittering theme (bars 351–2) which together with Don Juan's horn motif – now on glockenspiel and trumpet – sweeps the music into a powerful series of majestic statements, gaining progressively in force and momentum until at the climax it falls with a torrential sweep into a terrible pit (bar 423).

Psychological as this collapse is, it is indistinguishable in its dramatic orchestral language from the actual events described in the parallel climax towards the end of the work. Don Juan's morale has suddenly reached rock-bottom. The ghosts of his three former mistresses flit across his consciousness. In his despondency he has taken to wandering through churchyards and, as in Da Ponte, Lenau makes him invite to dinner the statue of a distinguished nobleman whom he has killed.

Lenau, however, is concerned not with the metaphysical but with reality. The statue does not come; it is the nobleman's son, Don Pedro, who intrudes upon the Supper Scene. He challenges the invincible libertine to a death duel and as the opening motif tentatively puts out feelers in the different string groups over a dominant pedal (bars 458ff) Don Juan gathers strength and confidence for the final stage of the drama, or in symphonic terms a partial recapitulation.

The logical construction is exemplary, its cumulative power overwhelming. From the opening of the recapitulation the music drives forward without a moment's hesitation from peak to peak until the appalling hiatus in which, at the height of his regained strength, Don Juan, with Pedro entirely at his mercy, realizes that victory is worthless and voluntarily delivers himself to the sword of his adversary. There is a pale minor chord into which the trumpets jab out the dissonant note representing with horrible clarity the mortal thrust (bar 587), and with a descending series of shuddering trills Don Juan's life ebbs away. The work ends on a note of blankness which is the more devastating for the closeness with which it follows on the heels of a scene of unparalleled splendour and exultation.

Although Strauss had at first had higher aims than Weimar for the première of *Don Juan*, he allowed himself to be prevailed upon rather than take the risk of waiting for some less certain occasion. This was wise both because the stir it created by its reception – even in a relatively small centre – was enough to arouse interest in the capital on which Strauss had fixed his hopes, and because the experience of taking a small and less proficient orchestra through the unprecedented difficulties of the piece enabled him to judge the practicability and effectiveness of his latest experiments in orchestration.

The first performance was on 11 November 1889, and he knew at once he had succeeded, and communicated his satisfaction in glowing letters to his parents. The players seem to have taken it well after the initial shock, though there were amusing incidents such as the remark of one horn player who, as he sat breathless and dripping with sweat, sighed: 'Lieber Gott! in what way have we sinned to have been sent this scourge!' Strauss wrote: 'We laughed till we cried! Certainly the horns blew without fear of death . . . I was really sorry for the poor horns and trumpets. They were quite blue in the face, the whole affair was so strenuous.'

The public response on that exciting day, 11 November 1889, is now a historical byword. The appearance of *Don Juan* established Strauss once and for all as the most important composer to have emerged in Germany since Wagner. At twenty-four Strauss had written the first of the master-pieces on which his position in musical history firmly rests.

Norman Del Mar

(Adapted from Norman Del Mar's *Richard Strauss – A critical survey of his life and works*, Vol. I, by kind permission of the publishers, Barrie and Jenkins.)

RICHARD STRAUSS
Don Juan

Der Zeitpunkt, an dem Strauss wirklich mit der Arbeit am *Don Juan* begonnen hat, lässt sich nicht genau ermitteln. Er selbst schrieb, dass er die ersten Themen im Mai 1888, auf der Reise nach Venedig, im Hof des Klosters von San Antonio in Padua, erfunden hat. Da es jedoch feststeht, dass das Werk noch im gleichen Sommer vollendet wurde, wäre dann nur eine unvorstellbar kurze Zeit für die Komposition einer derartig ausgearbeiteten und komplizierten Partitur übriggeblieben, und alle seine Biographen haben daher die Annahme gelten lassen, dass die ersten Entwürfe im Herbst 1887 skizziert worden sind.

Als Basis für seine Studie über dieses grosse erotische Thema, nahm Strauss das in Versen geschriebene Stück von Nikolaus Lenau, jedoch nicht so sehr um Lenaus dramatischer Behandlung des Stoffes willen, sondern vielmehr wegen seiner psychologischen Methode, das Wesen dieses berüchtigten Frauenjägers zu durchdringen. Lenaus *Don Juan* folgt dem Lebenslauf Don Juans von der Szene, in der sein Bruder Don Diego versucht, ihn zu überreden, sein der Sinnlichkeit gewidmetes Leben aufzugeben, und nach Hause zu kommen, bis zu dem Duell in dem er am Ende stirbt – nicht weil er der Besiegte ist, sondern weil er den Sieg ,,so langweilig findet wie das ganze Leben." Nach jeder seiner Taten erweist es sich, dass irgendein grosses Unheil daraus erwachsen ist, und Don Juans Einstellung zu den schlimmen Folgen lässt sich mit den Worten zusammenfassen, die er zu einem Kamerad sagt, nachdem er ein Kloster entweiht hat, das dann der Abt in seiner Verzweiflung ganz zerstört:
,,Das ging zuweit, so hab' ich's nicht gemeint.
Wer Böses tut, tut mehr stets, als er will . . .``

Die Art, in welcher Strauss diesen Stoff behandelt, ist aus den Zitaten zu ersehen, die er an den Anfang seiner Partitur stellt. Sie werden alle von Don Juan selbst gesprochen. Die ersten beiden stehen kurz hintereinander in der ersten Szene und stellen im wesentlichen Don Juans Gründe dafür dar, dass er die Bitte seines Bruders, unverzüglich nach Hause zu kommen, ausschlägt. Im ersten Zitat verkündet er seine Hingabe an den Augenblick, der nie wiederkehrt:
Den Zauberkreis, den unermesslich weiten,
Von vielfach reizend schönen Weiblichkeiten
Möcht' ich durchziehn im Sturme des Genusses,
Am Mund der letzten sterben eines Kusses.
O Freund, durch alle Räume möcht' ich fliegen,
Wo eine Schönheit blüht, hinknien vor jede
Und, wär's auch nur für Augenblicke, siegen.

Das hauptsächliche und ausführlichste Zitat ist Don Juans Antwort auf Diegos Worte, die ihn vor seinem unvermeidlichen Ende als Bettler warnen:

Ich fliehe Überdruss und Lustermattung,
Erhalte frisch im Dienste mich des Schönen,
Die einzle kränkend schwärm' ich für die Gattung.
Der Odem einer Frau, heut Frühlingsduft,
Drückt morgen mich vielleicht wie Kerkerluft.
Wenn wechselnd ich mit meiner Liebe wandle
Im weiten Kreis der schönen Frauen,
Ist meine Lieb' an jeder eine andre;
Nicht aus Ruinen will ich Tempel bauen.
Ja! Leidenschaft ist immer nur die neue;
Sie lässt sich nicht von der zu jener bringen,
Sie kann nur sterben hier, dort neu entspringen,
Und kennt sie sich, so weiss sie nichts von Reue.
Wie jede Schönheit einzig in der Welt,
So ist es auch die Lieb', der sie gefällt.
Hinaus und fort nach immer neuen Siegen.
So lang der Jugend Feuerpulse fliegen!

Das letzte der Zitate ist der letzten Szene mit dem Abendmahl entnommen, bei dem Don Juan, anders als Da Pontes Don Giovanni, voll düsterer Laune, und ganz seiner bitteren Enttäuschung hingegeben, dasitzt. Doch bedauert er immer noch nichts, und vermag das Weinen und Klagen der Reue nicht zu dulden:

Es war ein schöner Sturm, der mich getrieben,
Er hat vertobt und Stille ist geblieben.
Scheintot ist alles Wünschen, alles Hoffen;
Vielleicht ein Blitz aus Höh'n, die ich verachtet,
Hat tödlich meine Liebeskraft getroffen,
Und plötzlich ward die Welt mir wüst, umnachtet;
Vielleicht auch nicht; – der Brennstoff ist verzehrt,
Und kalt und dunkel ward es auf dem Herd.

Demnach enthalten die drei Zitate nichts aus der Handlung des Stücks. Sie sind rein psychologischer Art und veranschaulichen Strauss' Absicht, den Charakter Don Juans durch seine eigenen Worte darzustellen. Doch dienen sie nur teilweise als Einführung zu der Musik, die sich, im Gegenteil, in gewissem Masse mit der direkten Schilderung der dramatischen Episoden beschäftigt. Sie enthält zwei grosse Liebesszenen, eine Fastnacht und einen in sich klar abgeschlossenen Teil, in welchem, beim Höhepunkt des Duells, der siegreiche Don Juan sein Rapier fortwirft und den Todesstoss erhält. Von all dem sagt das von Strauss mitgeteilte Programm nichts aus, doch die scheinbare Unvereinbarkeit betont noch seine ganze Einstellung zum Thema. Einerseits ist *Don Juan* ein sinfonischer Satz, der nach den thematischen

Voraussetzungen völlig ausgearbeitet ist, andrerseits schildert er gleichzeitig die Entwicklung eines menschlichen Charakters unter dem Einfluss der Ereignisse, so wie es Strauss gerade im *Macbeth* getan hatte, dessen erste Fassung im gleichen Jahr (1888) vollendet wurde.

Selbst die Form des Werks ist grundsätzlich die gleiche wie die des *Macbeth*, d.h., es ist eine Sonatenform, wie sie in ersten Sätzen vorkommt, mit zwei grösseren, selbständigen Episoden in der Durchführung. Das Hauptthema (T. 1–6 und 9–16) besteht aus mehreren wesentlichen Teilen, die später isoliert und weitgehend entwickelt werden. Dieser Reichtum an Motiven stellt, als Ganzes gesehen, Don Juan selbst in aller seiner leidenschaftlichen Herrlichkeit und Lebenslust dar.

Ein weiteres, von den Bassinstrumenten zuerst in Takt 40 gespieltes Thema, drängt die Musik ungestüm voran und führt zu der ersten Liebelei des Helden. Diese Episode hat wenig Substanz und könnte fast als zu kurzlebig betrachtet werden, um die Bezeichnung Episode zu verdienen, wenn sie nicht später ihren Platz unter den anderen Liebesaffären in der Szene hätte, in welcher Don Juan sich bewusst ist, dass er keine Illusionen mehr hat (T. 427ff.). Das Thema dieser Heldin (T. 48–9) ist ganz kapriziös, und selbst der Hinweis *flebile* vermag nicht vorzutäuschen, dass ihr Herz dabei im Spiel war.

Doch mit der chromatisch absteigenden Figur, mit der sie von Don Juan Abschied nimmt (T. 53, Klarinette), hatte Strauss die Absicht, „ein Gefühl der Sättigung in Juans Herz" darzustellen, was darauf hindeutet, dass eine emotionale Bindung zwischen ihnen bestanden hat. Das zeigt sich in den Takten 46–7, welche jene Melodie im *fortissimo* enthalten, die später Don Juans erste echte Liebesszene dominiert.

Mit einer ungeduldigen, grossen Geste reisst er sich von dieser unbefriedigenden Geliebten los, dreht sich um und erliegt sogleich dem Zauber einer neuen Schönheit. Don Juan ist tief bewegt, und ihre Liebesszene folgt, die in einem gewaltig ausgedehnten Teil (T. 90–149) geschildert wird, und deren Leidenschaft nur mit einem solchen sinnlichen Entzücken, wie dem im zweiten Akt des *Tristan*, zu vergleichen ist. Strauss pflegte im Scherz zu sagen, es wäre offenbar, dass das Mädchen rote Haare hätte.

Wenn die erste Liebelei die Funktion einer Überleitung übernahm, so entspricht dieser Teil dem zweiten Thema, wobei selbst die Tonart hier die traditionsgemässe der Dominante ist. Die Musik erreicht einen Höhepunkt von unerträglicher Intensität, um plötzlich wieder abzuklingen, wobei die Celli Don Juans Anfangsthema einwerfen, als wäre es eine Frage. Er ist aus der Versunkenheit der Liebe erwacht, und obwohl die Geliebte alles tut, um seine Träume anhalten zu lassen, haben sie jetzt keine Macht mehr über ihn. Im Nu wird Don Juan unerreichbar und ist auf und davon, auf der Suche nach weiteren Abenteuern.

Die darauffolgende Passage ist ihrer Art nach reine Durchführung. In ihr erreichten Don Juans Themen einen ekstatischen Höhepunkt (T. 169–96). Dann kommt die Bewegung plötzlich zum Stillstand, und ein neues Liebeswerben beginnt. Diesmal kapituliert das Mädchen nicht so schnell, und Don Juans Umwerben erhält eine sehnsuchtvolle Intensität (T. 197–202), bis er allmählich ihren bemitleidenswerten Widerstand überwindet, und sie schliesslich ganz unterliegt.

So vollkommen ist ihre Hingabe, so rührend ihre Liebe, dass man sich fragen muss, wer diese, für die Geschichte so bedeutende Figur sein mag. Es lässt sich allerdings nicht feststellen, an welche der Heldinnen Lenaus Strauss dabei gedacht hat, da das Gedicht keine vergleichbare Episode enthält. Laut mindestens einer Version der Geschichte, ist es Donna Anna, die allein eine ernste Leidenschaft in Don Juans Leben darstellt. Aber bei Da Ponte sind seine Versuche sie zu verführen erfolglos, und bei Lenau wird sie kaum erwähnt. Wie dem auch sei, es besteht nicht der geringste Zweifel, dass Strauss hier Don Juans tiefstes Liebeserlebnis behandelt. Die Takte von T. 232 bis 306 gehören zu den grossartigsten Liebesliedern der gesamten Musikliteratur.

Das Ende des Lieds ist zugleich das Ende der ersten Hälfte der sinfonischen Dichtung, und Strauss mag sich darüber Gedanken gemacht haben, wie er die Fortsetzung gestalten sollte. Seine Lösung dieses Problems hat Geschichte gemacht. Er schuf diese Lösung, indem er ein neues Motiv für Don Juan erfand, und zwar ein Hornsignal für vier Hörner, das bis auf den heutigen Tag das Thema geblieben ist, das sofort die Vorstellung der ganzen sinfonischen Dichtung erweckt (T. 314–26). Jetzt ist Don Juan nicht mehr nur kühn und ungestüm – er ist ein Held geworden.

Genau wie die frühere Geliebte klammert sich das arme Mädchen an Don Juan, aber sie hat noch weniger Macht über ihn als ihre Vorgängerinnen. Don Juan ist sowieso schon eifrig bei etwas anderem. Er stürzt sich, bei einer blendenden Prachtentfaltung der Orchesterfarben, mitten in irgendein wildes Fest.

Dieser zweite Durchführungsteil (T. 351–423) ist allgemein als Fastnachtszene bekannt, obwohl bei Lenau von Szenen dieser Art nur ein Maskenball zu finden ist. Ein neues, strahlendes Thema (T. 351–2) reisst, zusammen mit Don Juans Hornmotiv – hier vom Glockenspiel und der Trompete gespielt – die Musik bis zu einer mächtigen Reihe von Phrasen majestätischen Charakters mit sich und gewinnt ständig an Kraft und Geschwindigkeit, bis es, am Höhepunkt angelangt, sturzähnlich in einen furchtbaren Abgrund fällt (T. 423).

So psychologischer Art dieser Zusammenbruch auch sein mag, er lässt sich, wie er dramatisch durch das Orchester ausgedrückt wird, nicht von den Ereignissen unterscheiden, die bei dem entsprechenden Höhepunkt gegen Ende des Stücks beschrieben werden. Don Juan ist plötzlich moralisch ganz niedergedrückt. Die Schatten seiner drei früheren Geliebten schwirren an seinem Geist vorbei. In seiner Verzweiflung hat er sich angewöhnt, in Friedhöfen umherzuwandern, und wie Da Ponte, lässt Lenau ihn das Standbild eines vornehmen Edelmanns, den er getötet hat, zum Essen einladen.

Lenau gibt sich jedoch nicht mit dem Metaphysischen sondern mit der Wirklichkeit ab. Das Standbild kommt nicht. Es ist der Sohn des Edelmanns, Don Pedro, der bei der Abendmahlszene störend eindringt. Er fordert den unbesieglichen Wüstling zu einem Duell auf den Tod, und während das Anfangsmotiv über einem Orgelpunkt auf der Dominante seine Fühler ausstreckt (T. 458ff.), sammelt Don Juan Kraft und Zuversicht für die letzten Abschnitte des Dramas oder, sinfonisch gesprochen, für die partielle Reprise.

Der logische Aufbau ist vorbildlich, seine kumulative Macht überwältigend. Ohne einen Moment zu zögern, stürzt die Musik vom Anfang der Reprise an vorwärts und von einem Höhepunkt zum andern, bis zu dem entsetzlichen Bruch, bei welchem Don Juan – nun voller wiedergewonnener Kraft, so dass Pedro ganz seiner Gnade ausgeliefert ist – begreift, dass Siegen wertlos ist, worauf er sich freiwillig dem Schwertstoss seines Gegners darbietet. Die Trompeten versetzen einem fahlen Mollakkord den Stich einer Dissonanz, die in furchtbarer Klarheit den Todesstoss darstellt (T. 587). Mit einer Reihe schaudernder Triller verebbt Don Juans Leben. Das Werk endet mit einem Gefühl der Leere, die, weil sie direkt auf eine Szene von unvergleichlichem Glanz und Entzücken folgt, umso verheerender wirkt.

Obgleich Strauss zunächst für die Premiere des *Don Juan* höher gezielt hatte als Weimar, liess er sich überreden, anstatt es zu riskieren auf eine weniger sichere Gelegenheit zu warten. Das erwies sich als weise, denn erstens war das Aufsehen, das sein Erfolg – wenn auch in einem relativ kleinen Rahmen – erzielte, gross genug, um das Interesse am Werk in der Hauptstadt, auf die Strauss als Aufführungsort gehofft hatte, zu erwecken, und zweitens, weil er dadurch, dass er die unerhörten Schwierigkeiten des Stücks mit einem kleinen und weniger erfahrenen Orchester durcharbeiten konnte, in der Lage war, die Durchführbarkeit und Wirkung seiner neusten Instrumentierungsexperimente zu beurteilen.

Die Erstaufführung fand am 11. November 1889 statt. Strauss war sich sofort seines Erfolgs bewusst und teilte seine Genugtuung seinen Eltern in begeisterten Briefen mit. Nach dem ersten Schock, scheinen die Musiker das Stück gut aufgenommen zu haben. Doch kam es zu amüsanten Vorfällen, wie dem, als ein Hornist atemlos und schweisstriefend dasass und seufzte: „Du lieber Gott! Was haben wir denn verbrochen, dass du uns diese Rute (das bin ich) geschickt hast!" Strauss schrieb: „Wir haben Tränen gelacht! Dabei haben die Hornisten mit Todesverachten geblasen! . . . Die armen Hornisten und Trompeter taten mir wirklich leid. Die bliesen sich ganz blau, so anstrengend ist die Geschichte."

Die Reaktion des Publikums an diesem aufregenden Tag, dem 11. November 1889, ist nun in die Geschichte eingegangen. Durch *Don Juan* hatte es sich ein für alle Mal erwiesen, dass Strauss der bedeutendste deutsche Komponist seit Wagner war. Im Alter von vierundzwanzig Jahren hatte er das erste jener Meisterwerke komponiert, auf denen sein Platz in der Musikgeschichte fest begründet ist.

NORMAN DEL MAR
Deutsche Übersetzung Stefan de Haan

(Vorliegender Text ist ein Auszug aus Norman Del Mars *Richard Strauss – A critical survey of his life and works,* 1. Bd, mit freundlicher Genehmigung der Verleger Barrie and Jenkins.)

ORCHESTRA.

8 Flauti (Flauto 8 anche Flauto Piccolo), 2 Oboi, Corno Inglese, 2 Clarinetti in La (A), 2 Fagotti,
Contrafagotto, 4 Corni, 3 Trombe, 3 Tromboni, Tuba.

Violini I, Violini II, Viole, Violoncelli, Contrabassi, Arpa.

8 Timpani in Mi, Si, Do (E, H, C), Triangolo, Piatti, Campanelle.

ABKÜRZUNGEN:	ABBREVIATIONS:	ABRÉVIATIONS:	ABBREVIAZIONI
Kl. Fl. ....Kleine Flöte	Piccolo	Petite Flûte	Ottavino
Gr. Fl. ....Große Flöt	Flute	Flûte	Flauto
Ob........Hobo	Oboe	Hautbois	Oboe
Englh.....Engli ch Horn	English Horn	Cor Anglais	Corno Inglese
Kl.*)......Klarinette	Clarinet	Clarinette	Clarinetto
Fag.......Fagott	Bassoon	Basson	Fagotto
K. Fag. ...Kontrafagott	Contrabassoon	Contrabasson	Contrafagotto
Hr.*) ......Horn	Horn	Cor	Corno
Trp. ....Trompete	Trumpet	Trompette	Tromba
Pos. ....Posaune	Trombone	Trombone	Trombone
Tb. ....Baßtuba	Bass Tuba	Tuba basse	Tuba bassa
Vl. ....Violine	Violin	Violon	Violino
Br. ....Bratsche	Viola	Alto	Viola
Vlc. ....Violoncello	Violoncello	Violoncelle	Violoncello
Kb........Kontrabaß	Double bass	Contrabasse	Contrabasso
Hfe.......Harfe	Harp	Harpe	Arpa
Pk.*) ......Pauke	Kettle drum	Timbale	Timpani
Trgl. ......Triangel	Triangle	Triangle	Triangolo
Bck........Becken	Cymbal	Cymbales	Piatti
Glsp. ......Glockenspiel	Set of bells	Carillon	Campanelle

	*) in A — in La	in E — in Mi
	in B — in Si ♭	in F — in Fa
	in C — in Do	in H — in Si

Mit Holzschlägeln . . .	con bacchette di legno	weich	dolce
Mit Schwammschlägeln . .	con bacchette di spugna	Vierfach (dreifach) geteilt divisi in 4 (in 3)	
gewöhnlich	ordinario	Dreitaktig	ritmo di 3 battute
Die Hälfte	la metà	Viertaktig	ritmo di 4 battute
Fis nach E umstimmen	fa ♯ muta in mi	Offen	aperto
G nach Fis umstimmen	sol muta in fa ♯	Gestopft	chiuso

Don Juan.

Tondichtung für großes Orchester.

Richard Strauss, Op. 20.
(1864-1949)

E. E. 3499

12

E. E. 3499

[1] sic in the original percussion part and always played, although it is missing in the score

E. E. 3499

E. E. 3499

E. E. 3499

28

122

128
F
1.2.gr.Fl.
3.gr.Fl.
1.2.Ob.
Englh.
1.2.Kl. (A)
1.2.Fag.
K. Fag.
1.2.H. (E)
3.4.H. (E)
Hfe.
1.Vl.
2.Vl.
Br.
Vlc.
Kb.
molto espr.
cresc.
espr.

135

molto appassionato e sempre un poco stringendo

tempo vivo e poco stringendo

168
H
1.2.gr.Fl.
3.gr.Fl.
1.2.Ob.
Englh.
1.2.Kl. (A)
1.2.Fag.
K.-Fag.
1.2.H. (E)
3.4.H. (E)
1.2.Trp. (E)
3. Trp. (E)
1.2.Pos.
3.Pos. Tb.
Pk.
Trgl. Bck.
Beck. mit Holzschl.
1.Vl.
2.Vl.
Br.
Vlc.
Kb.
pizz.
pizz.

E. E. 3499

187
1.2.gr.Fl.
3.gr.Fl.
ff
kl. Flöte
1.2.Ob.
Englh.
1.2.Kl. (A)
1.2.Fag.
ff
K.-Fag.
ff
1.2.H. (E.)
f
3.4.H. (E.)
f
1.2.Trp. (E.)
f
3. Trp. (E.)
f
Trgl. Bck.
Hfe.
1. Vl.
pizz.
arco
2. Vl.
pizz.
arco
Br.
pizz.
arco
Vlc.
pizz.
arco
Kb.
arco
ff

190

E. E. 3499

New subj.
234
sehr getragen und ausdrucksvoll
Solo.
p
1.2. Ob.
K. Fag.
1.2. H. (F)
pp
Pk.
Hfe.
1. Vl.
pp
Br.
Vlc.
Kb.
240
1.2. Ob.
1.2. Kl. (B)
pp
K.-Fag.
1.2. H. (F)
con sord.
p
3.4. H. (F)
con sord.
p
Pk.
Hfe.
1. Vl.
2. Vl.
pp
Br.
pp
Vlc.
2.
1.
1.
2.
pp
Kb.
pp

E. E. 3499

E. E. 3499

E. E. 3499

E. E. 3499

stringendo

347

development section

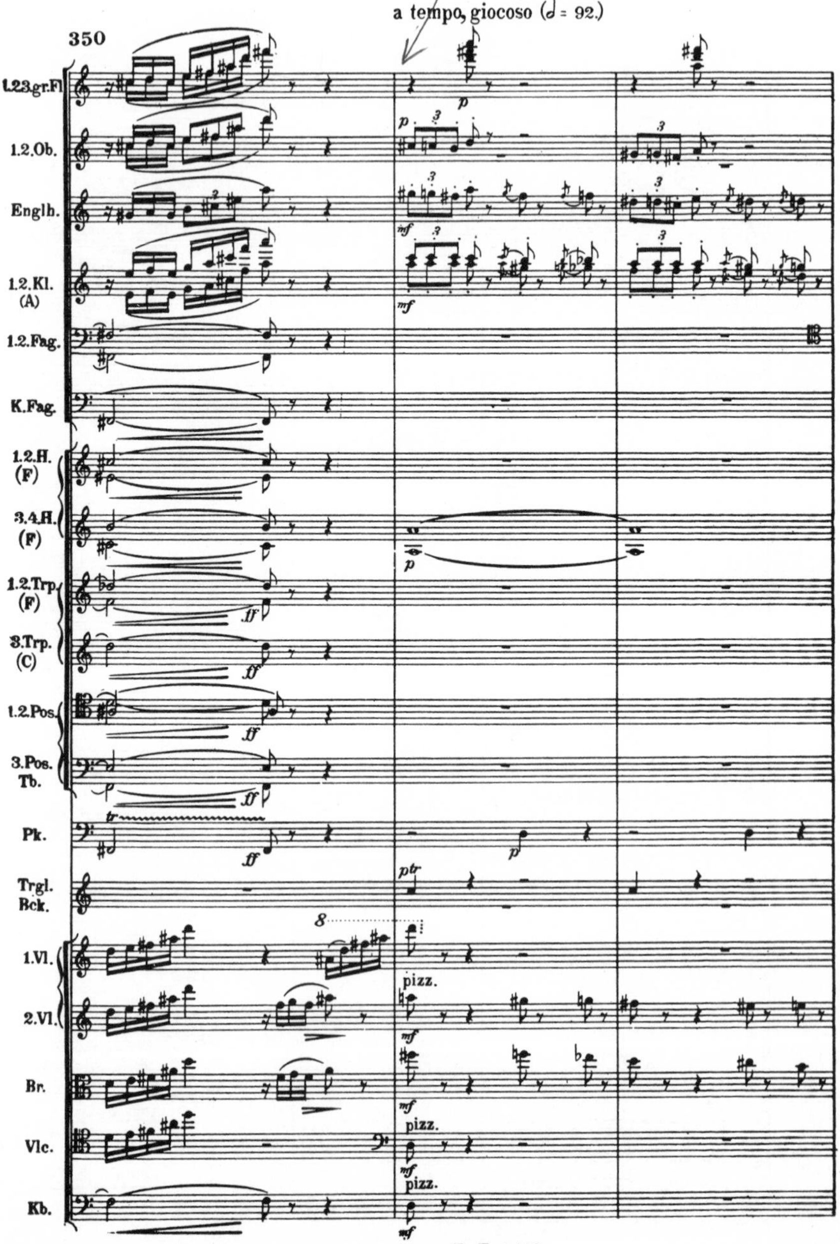

E. E. 3499

E. E. 3499

E. E. 3499

E. E. 3499

poco più agitato

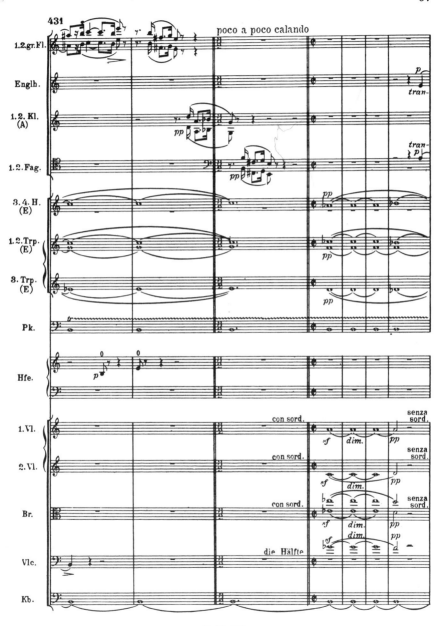

E. E. 3499

E. E. 3499

E. E. 3499

527

531

539

animato

Dreitaktig. poco a poco più animato.

E. E. 3499

552

E. E. 3499

più stringendo

(♩ = 72)

tempo primo, poco a poco più lento, ma sempre alla breve.

586

Dd

594

597

sempre più lento.